solo repertoire

by Jane Smisor Bastien

Preface

SOLO REPERTOIRE consists of twenty-two original solos that may be used as supplementary material for the Older Beginner. The compositions have a variety of keys and progress in order of difficulty through Levels 1 and 2 of the **OLDER BEGINNER PIANO LIBRARY.**

 NEIL A. KJOS, JR., PUBLISHER • San Diego, California

Published by Kjos West, 4382 Jutland Dr., San Diego, CA 92117

ISBN 0-8497-5172-1

❧ CONTENTS ❧

DEBUT

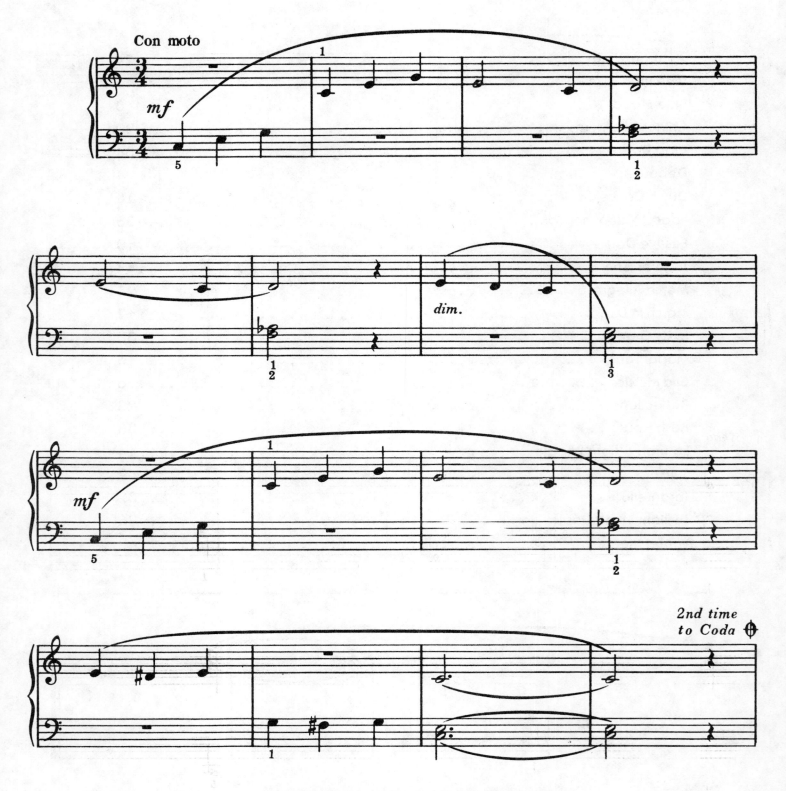

❁ OLD MEXICO ❁

Con spirito

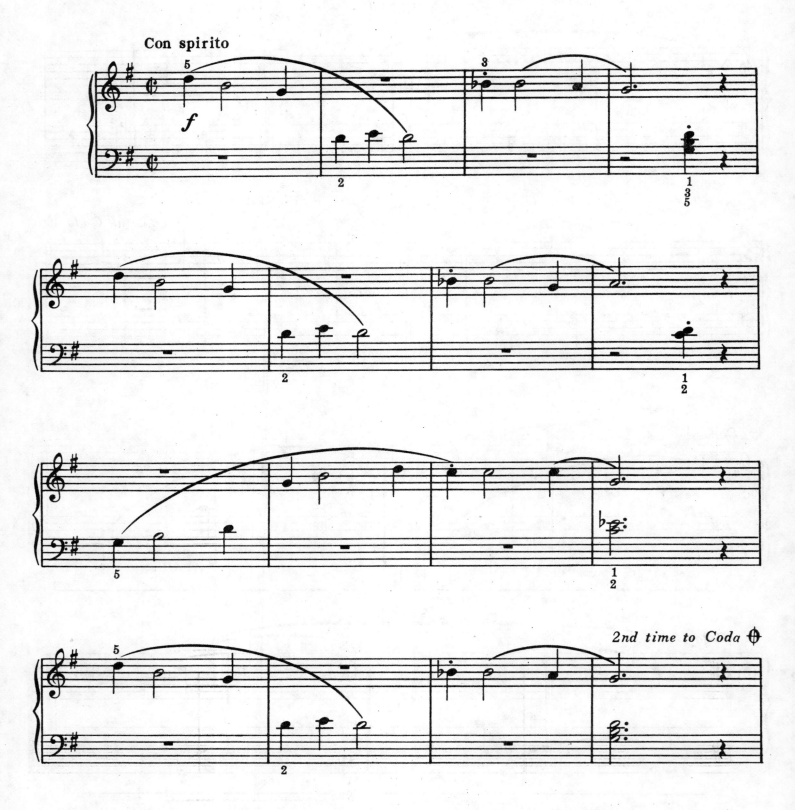

BLUE MOOD

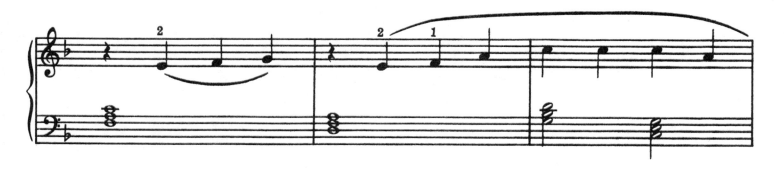

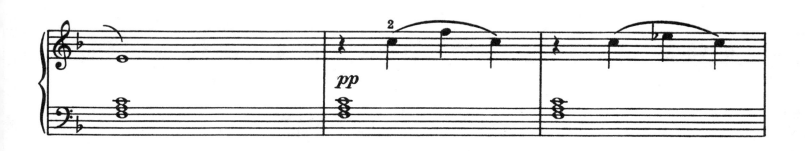

FESTIVE DANCE

❄ MARCH IN D ❄

SATURDAY NIGHT BOOGIE

MODAL SONG

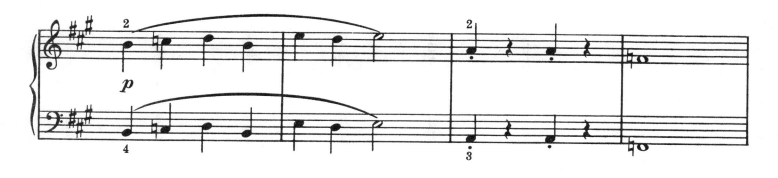

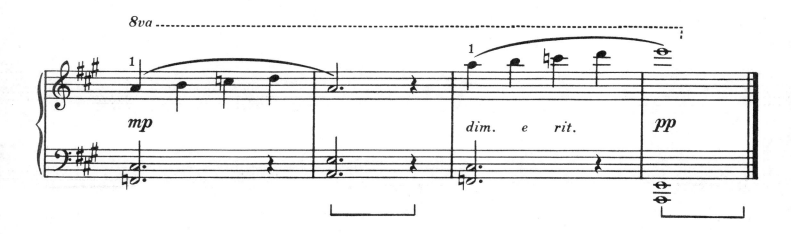

❈ DUTCH DANCE ❈

CHINESE LANTERNS

REFLECTIONS

AUTUMN WINDS

WP83

TWILIGHT IN THE DESERT

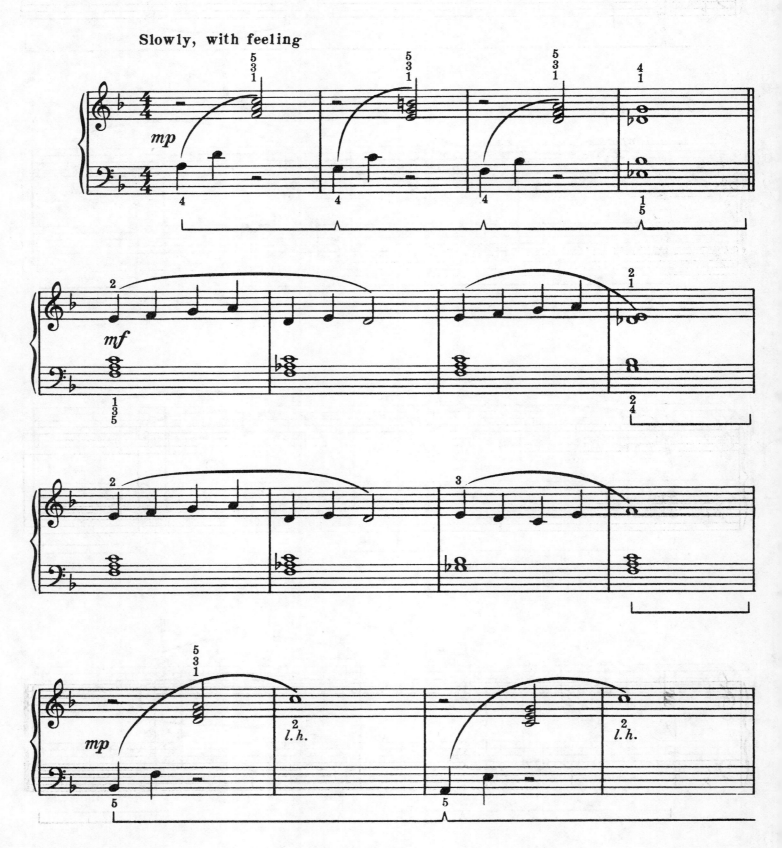

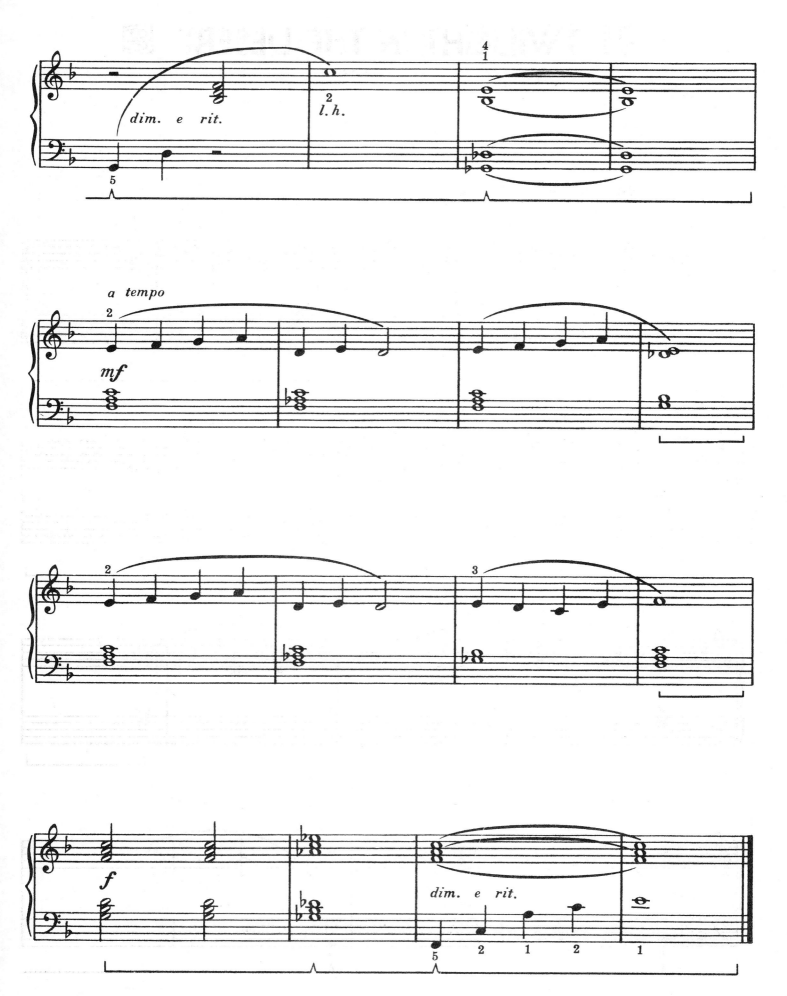

MARCH ALLEGRO

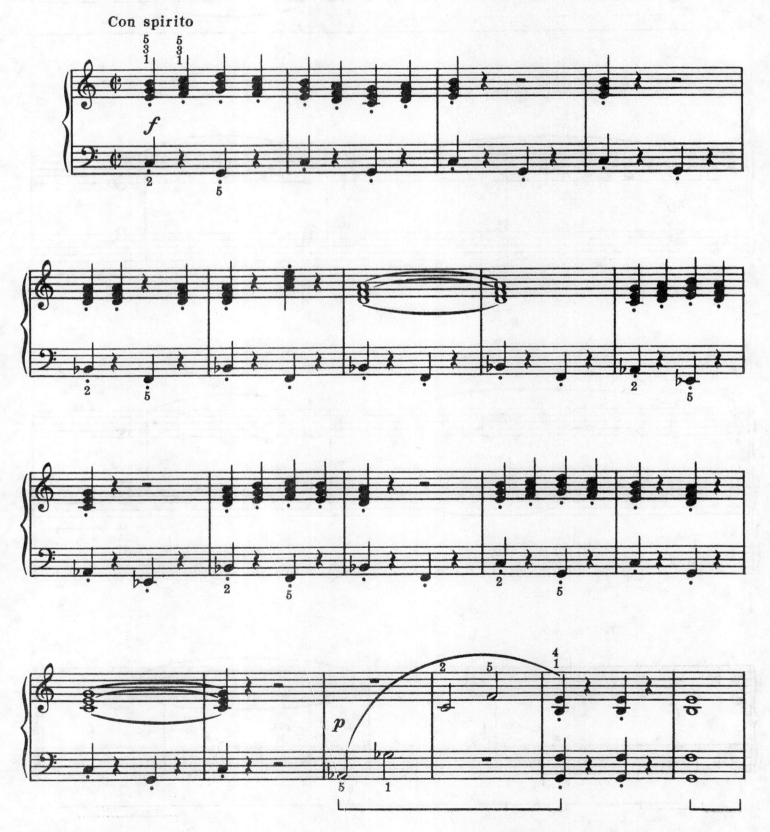

❄ MISTY GREEN ❄

TARANTELLA

CLOG DANCE

Allegro con spirito

FADED VALENTINE

Slowly and thoughtfully

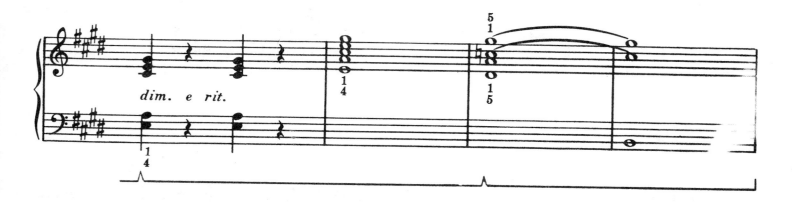

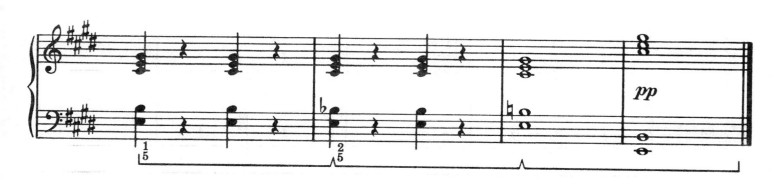

WP83

RUSH HOUR

◆ WINTER MEMORY ◆

Slowly, but with motion

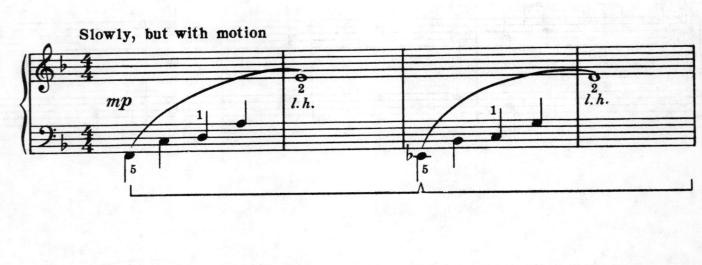

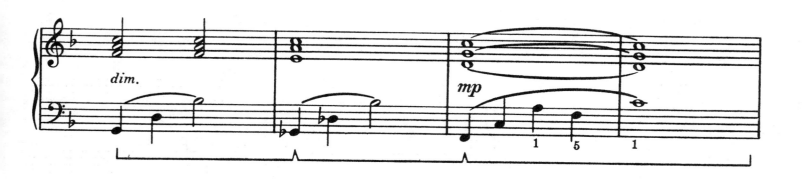

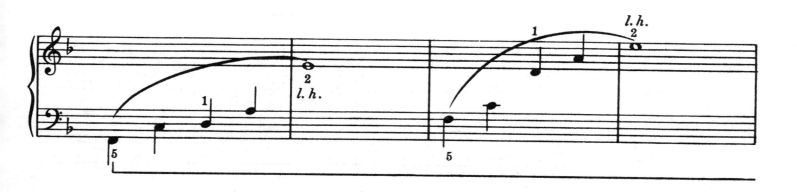

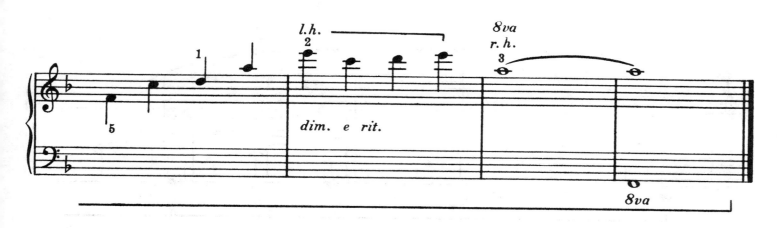

WP83

❀ SUNSET ❀

WP83

44

THE JUGGLER

Allegro con spirito

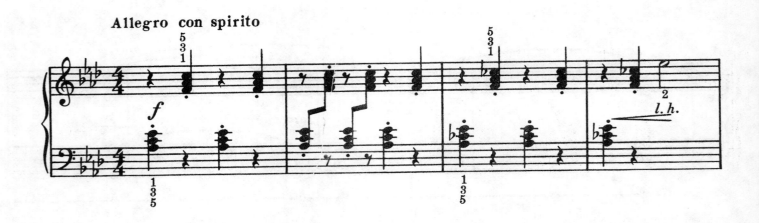

WP83

BLUE IRIS

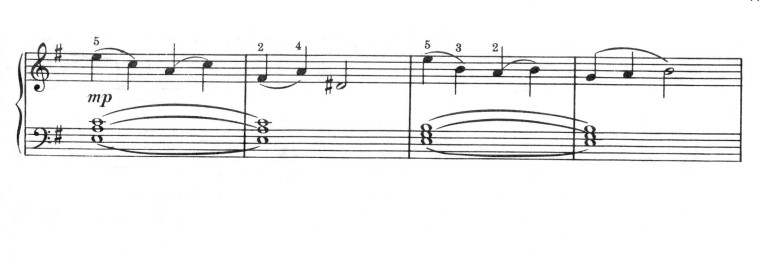